1 2 3 4 5 6 7 8 9 0

Absolutely
Mental
2

Also by Rowland Morgan

Absolutely Mental 1

Number Crunchers: Brain Bafflers

1 2 3 4 5 6 7 8 9 0

Absolutely Mental 2

Rowland Morgan

Illustrated by
Mike Phillips

MACMILLAN CHILDREN'S BOOKS

First published 2000
by Macmillan Children's Books
a division of Macmillan Publishers Ltd
25 Eccleston Place, London SW1W 9NF
Basingstoke and Oxford
www.macmillan.co.uk

Associated companies throughout the world

ISBN 0 330 48173 8

1 3 5 7 9 8 6 4 2

A CIP catalogue record for this book is available from the British Library.

Printed by Mackays of Chatham plc, Chatham, Kent.

1 2 3 4 5 6 7 8 9 0

Contents

1 2 3 4 5 6 7 8 9 0

Absolutely Mental:
Introduction

There have been many theories that maths was invented by aliens from outer space. These theories are hard to disprove because we know so little about how prehistoric people thought about figures. What we do know is that the ancient Greeks thought numbers were holy. People who worked with them were considered magicians. Figuring was kept secret and believed to be a weird power, like witchcraft. The Greeks left it to other countries to develop numbers, such as Sumeria, Babylon, China, India and eastern Arabia. For about two thousand years, science was regarded superstitiously in Europe. And that's why maths, even today, has a special genius status that it does not deserve. But medical tests suggest that, far from being a genius subject, maths is "hard-wired" into the human brain. Yes, you're actually born with a calculator fitted in your head!

Here are numerous examples of mental arithmetic in living colour, showing how numbers are not only built in to our brains, but built in to life. And showing how they can be lifesavers – if you can think quickly enough!

rowland@splong.com

1 2 3 4 5 6 7 8 9 0

Air Show

It was Maggie's first-ever air show. She had worked for the *Daily Planet* for several years, but the aviation reporter, Fred Wing, had called in sick the day before, and she was standing in for him. It was a big chance for Maggie. If she made a good job of this then she might be promoted. The new Prang fighter plane was being demonstrated for the first time today. Development of the plane had cost billions.

She checked her handbook once more and read the following information:

"An aeroplane travelling at less than Mach 1 is travelling at subsonic speeds. At about Mach 1 it is travelling at transonic speeds, or approximately the speed of sound. An aeroplane travelling at speeds greater than Mach 1 is travelling at supersonic speeds. For example, an aircraft flying at Mach 2 is travelling at twice the speed of sound."

The announcer on the public address system told the huge crowd that the Prang aeroplane would fly past in one minute. Maggie could see it as a glinting speck in the far distance. As it came closer the crowd could hear little more than a hiss. Then, as it went by, the most shattering roar and a terrifying noise hit the people. BA-BANG!

When she had recovered from the shock, Maggie stared after the plane. There was nothing but a slight smear of engine vapour hanging in the sky. She turned to her satellite link and started typing:

"Europe's new war toy, the £100-billion Euro fighter called Prang, made a sensational debut at the Paris air show today. Zooming over a crowd of 100,000 people at Mach 1, it created a massive double blast of sound, scaring most people out of their wits. If this plane was built to terrify civilians, the money was well spent."

That was Maggie's first paragraph. It cost her her job.

Why?

1 2 3 4 5 6 7 8 9 0

Barbells

Herbie Blugg the weightlifter flexed his muscles and looked down at the set of barbells. There were three weights at either end of the chrome bar. Thirty, twenty and fifteen kilos.

Herbie looked round at the crowd. The audience consisted of 70,000 people in the seats and there were another 500 million people watching from armchairs in front of the television. The cameras would be close up on him now. They'd be transmitting every bead of sweat on his brow.

He pushed his huge shoulders back and jutted out his jaw. Why play it down? He eyed the barbells again. He was in no hurry. He was the champion. OK, they were saying he was over the hill, played out, done for – but let them write what they liked. Let them spout what they wanted on the TV. What did they know about muscle? What did they know about sinew? What did they know about superhuman strength and will-power? Nothing!

In his mind he ran through the incredible task that lay ahead of him, under the heat of the TV lights. First, he must carry out the squat-style grab. Then the jerk with split. Then the unbelievable maintained lift, in which Herbie must hold 110 kilos at arm's length above his head, with every massive muscle in his body bulging.

He breathed deeply, wiped his forehead, coated his palms with resin and bent down to grip the cold bar.

A hush fell over the stadium.

Herbie took the strain, heaved, and suddenly realized something terrible that made his eyes blaze with fury.

What was it?

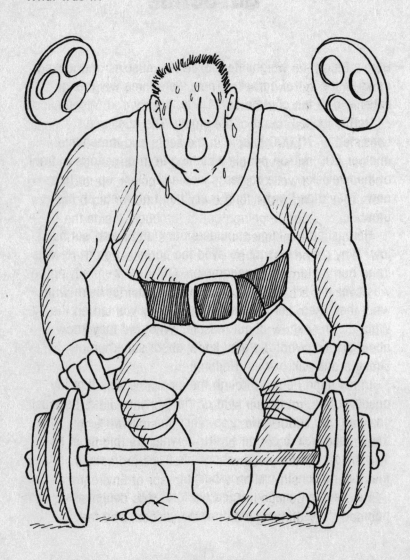

Bathtime

Ho Chi suffered from a nasty skin condition, so his doctor told him to go and live in the desert, where the sun would be good for his bad skin.

So he moved to the desert and built a house on a slope with a lovely view of the sea. The house was thatched with a roof of palm leaves, and was called a palapa. Next to it, he installed a wall of solar panels for power. He ordered big jars of drinking water for the kitchen, and for his bathroom he built a separate palapa out at the back. Inside the bathhouse, he installed a fine old cast iron bath with claws for feet that he had inherited from his ancestors. His mother had bathed him in it, and he loved it.

Behind the bathhouse, his builder constructed a large water tank, bought from an abandoned railway yard. Ho Chi called up the water company and asked them to send over a water tanker to fill up his bathroom tank. Next day, a big lorry arrived. It had a tractor unit that hauled a trailer that consisted of a long tank. Ho Chi had seen lorries like it delivering petrol to fuel stations. The driver said it carried 20 tonnes, or 20,000 litres of water. Ho smiled. He would have plenty of water for baths, even in the middle of the desert. When the place was finished, he promptly invited his son, Minh, to stay. Minh was Professor of Environment at Environment College in California. He was delighted with the palapas, the drinking water in the kitchen, and the solar

13

panels in the yard. But he frowned at the bath in the bath-house.

"Dad, this is out of order," he said.

"It works perfectly," his father protested. "What can go wrong with a bath?"

"I mean, you can't have it," Minh stated. "It uses far too much water."

"Nonsense, I have that enormous tank of water, it will last me for years. I have two baths a day. It's vital for my skin."

"I'm afraid that bath is a hundred litres. Your water will only last a hundred days."

Ho squinted. He couldn't decide what to do.

Was Minh right?

1 2 3 4 5 6 7 8 9 0

The Blurby Case

James Blurby ran the Pink Mountains Hotel uneventfully for many years. But one day there was a murder in a first floor bedroom and Blurby was charged with the crime. The evidence weighed heavily against him and it looked as if Blurby was on his way to prison. Until the confusion about the bedroom came up.

When the case came to court, six months after the event, Officer Flood of the police squad stated that the crime had taken place on the first floor. The defence then asked him the following question:

"For the jury, can you locate in which room exactly the body was found, based on the layout of the building? We know eight rooms are ranged on each side of the corridor. The stairs come up between the rooms numbered four and six. Even numbered rooms are on the stairs side."

"Certainly," said the over-confident policeman. He then plunged into a set of instructions that the court reporter had difficulty understanding:

"On the first floor, turn right and proceed as far as room 18. It was in this room that the body was found."

The court gasped. They saw a hole opening up and the case for the prosecution falling deep into it. The prosecution could do nothing to dislodge the reasonable doubt that this evidence raised in the minds of the jury.

Why?

Canyon

Rita Craig was a keen mountain climber. In particular, she loved to climb cliffs. She spent a lot of time climbing in canyons. She had quite a few scrapes. One day, when she asked her boyfriend, Dale, to sign her latest plaster-cast, he said to her, "That's the fifth time you've broken an arm or a leg. Aren't you sick of it by now?"

She thought it over and admitted that she was.

"Then why don't you practise hanging from cliff-edges, until your fingers are so strong that you never make a mistake?" Dale asked.

Rita lay awake that night. Next day, she called a builder and had an artificial cliff-face built in her garden. It was only three metres high. She stood just under two metres, so when she let go, she did not have far to fall. She practised all that winter, hanging by eight fingers until her knuckles went white. She timed herself, and managed to extend her endurance from two minutes to 24.6 minutes – an almost incredible feat. She practised hanging by one hand (four fingers) as well, and reached a remarkable 14.3 minutes at that. Just out of interest, she practised hanging by one finger (the index), but achieved only 3.2 seconds. By the time the next climbing season came round, she felt ready to climb real cliffs once more.

Rita took a jet flight to her favourite canyon-lands in America, and drove a rented car to the canyons, in the middle of nowhere. Then she put on her boots and walked still further. Finally, she put on her climbing boots and climbed high above the ground. She found it thrilling to be so alone. Until she fell.

She fell through the air, hearing a terrifying rushing sound in her ears. Suddenly, a cliff-edge came zooming up, and she grabbed for it. Her fingers were so strong from all the training that she jolted to a halt, dangling by eight fingers. She stayed calm. She knew exactly how long she could last. She had only to call for help.

She removed one hand from the cliff-edge and took out her mobile phone. She had programmed the rescue number in to it, so she only had to press one button with her thumb. They replied immediately, and quickly took the map co-ordinates of her position.

"We'll have a chopper there by five past the hour," they promised. "Trust us."

Rita could only afford a quick glance at the time displayed on her phone: 11.40, before she put it away and clung on with both hands again.

She dangled there by eight fingers, trying to work out if she could hold on until the rescue services arrived. Each time she looked down and saw the immense distance to the bottom of the canyon, a sheer drop, it took her mind off the figures.

At last she had to give in. She could hold on no longer. She let go, just as the helicopter came into view.

What was Rita's mistake?

1 2 3 4 5 6 7 8 9 0

Cat

"The big cat, like all felines, walks on its toes," said Professor Finney. "This is clear from the footprints you can see here." The professor's sun-tanned finger pointed to marks in the dusty trail. She stood with a small group of students in the arid African countryside.

Toby was anxious to impress Professor Finney. He wanted her to consider him the most brilliant student ever to attend the college's summer school on African nature.

"The cat is notable for having five toes on its front paws and four at the back," continued Professor Finney. "How could that help us, when tracking a cat?"

Toby raised his hand to answer, but that annoying Rebecca butted in first, without raising her hand and waiting. "You can tell which direction it's going in, Professor?" she said.

"Yes, it helps," the professor replied, to Toby's disgust. "You can also identify more easily the number of cats you are tracking. How many toes does a cat have altogether then, Toby?"

Toby froze. He stared at his teacher. Now everything hung on his answer. He could not let Professor Finney down. Luckily, he thought quickly and produced the right answer for her.

What did he say?

Change

Jo lived in a tough neighbourhood. In the city where he lived shopkeepers were so nervous of burglaries that their shop windows were fitted with grilles and there were bars on the doors, like cages.

Jo hung out on the corner of 156th Street and 82nd after school (if he didn't skip class). He bought gum and candies from the corner store there. It was run by a tall, slow-moving man named Mo Williams.

One day, Mo came out on to the street and called to the boys on the street corner, "Hey, boys, I have to go out for a while. Which one of you wants to mind the store?" He pointed at Jo. Jo thought about it for a minute, and said, "All right."

Mo showed Jo how to work the counter. "Now you mind out for tricksters and their con tricks," Moe warned him. "Don't fall for them or you'll be a laughing stock in this neighbourhood."

Jo had not been standing long at the counter when a man in dark glasses entered the shop. "Hey, you got change for a twenty?" he said, holding out a twenty-dollar bill.

Jo held it under the black-light, the way Mo had told him. It looked OK.

"Sure," he said, and handed the customer two ten-dollar bills.

"Do me a favour, change that ten for two fives, will you?" the customer said.

Jo took one of the tens and gave back two fives. "Is that all?" he said.

"Just let me have five ones for this five," the man said.

Jo took back a five and counted out five ones. The man thanked him and left the shop.

The moment the customer had gone, Jo got a nasty feeling. He could see Mo counting the balance and going crazy. He could hear his friends shrieking with laughter. He could see his reputation being permanently damaged. Then the door banged open – it was Mo.

Did Jo make a mistake when handing over the change?

1 2 3 4 5 6 7 8 9 0

Concert

Angie couldn't decide what shoes to wear. She tried on every pair she owned but nothing seemed right.

Bugs couldn't manage to choose a top. He thought a T-shirt might be too cold, but he didn't like either of his sweatshirts any more. His two button-up shirts were too smart. He only wore them for weddings and family occasions when he had to.

Tank was having trouble with his belt. Should he wear the studded one with the badge? Or the Mexican one with a rattlesnake head that his dad had brought back from holiday? Or what about using a ropey old neck-tie from the bottom of his closet?

Dad sat in the car outside, fretting. He thought that it had been pretty generous of him to pay for three tickets to the show in the first place, without having to drive them there, to the other side of the city, as well. Then there was the extra money they would need for refreshments, and he would have to kill three hours in some movie he didn't want to see, or some coffee shop he didn't know, until they came out. To top it all, they still weren't ready. He opened the driver's window.

"Raphaella!" he bawled towards the house. "What is going on?"

His wife went to the foot of the stairs and shouted at her children, "You lot! Your father is waiting! Get going!"

Finally they were on the move. Angie said, "Hurry up, Dad."

Her father ground his teeth and growled, "First you keep me waiting for the best part of an hour, now you're worrying about being late."

Tank had his laptop open. He'd fed the details into a trip planner. "It's 29 kilometres to the stadium," he said.

"We're travelling at 62 km per hour," said Bugs, leaning over to see the speedometer.

"It's 7.58 p.m. now, and the show starts at 8.30 p.m.," screamed Angie. "We'll never make it! I'll never forgive you if we miss the band!"

"We'll make it," Dad said firmly.

The kids stared at him.

Did he get there in time?

The Dare

Rory O'Sullivan was the biggest man in the Irish village where he lived. He had the biggest mouth for talking, the biggest voice for singing and the biggest nerve when it came to a dare.

At sixteen, he fell in love with Maureen O'Grady, but unfortunately she did not feel the same way. Maureen was very similar to Rory in many ways. She showed off, she shouted, and she sang like an angel, everywhere she went.

One Sunday afternoon, all the lads were gathered on the harbour-front, joking around. Rory was boasting that Maureen was his girlfriend, when who should walk up but Maureen herself, with her friend.

"I heard what you were saying, Rory O'Sullivan," she said, bold as brass in front of the boys, "and I'll give you a dare if you'll take it."

Rory was not about to back down in front of the village, so he puffed out his chest and replied, "I don't care what the dare is, I'll take it."

Maureen pointed from her jeans to his and said in a clear voice, "Walk the length of the front wearing only half of your trousers."

Rory turned pale. "And . . . and you'll do the same?" he faltered.

"That I will," replied the bold young woman.

Rory saw she meant business and there was no way that he could back down from a dare. "Right you are," he said.

There was a hum of excitement among the boys. One of them produced a pocket knife to cut up Rory's trousers. The public toilets were right at hand.

"You go first," Maureen said. "And only half, mind."

Rory went into the toilets and emerged a few moments later with a red face, wearing one leg of his trousers, one pocket and half of the seat. Only his belt held the garment up. Everyone burst out laughing and jeering, pointing at the holes in his tattered underpants.

"Now it's your turn," Rory said, through gritted teeth, and they all fell silent as Maureen went into the ladies' toilets.

Did Maureen manage to protect her modesty?

1 2 3 4 5 6 7 8 9 0

DJ King

DJ King loved playing at the Freezer. Every night the club attracted a queue of people that went down the street, round the corner, across the pedestrian crossing, into the railway station and along the railway line.

The club was so well-known that it had no sign outside showing its name. There was only a big poster pasted to the wall advertising that DJ King played there.

DJ King worked hard to live up to stardom. He knew that there were hundreds of DJs nearly as good as him who were trying to climb up that slippery pole of fame. To keep up with new music trends, he listened to new music tracks for four hours every day.

Now he was deep into his gig, and his head was spinning. The music was so loud that the walls of the club pumped in time with the beat.

The trouble was, the club opened later than it should and violated noise pollution regulations. If the music did not end at 4.30 a.m. precisely, then the police would come and confiscate the DJ's sound equipment. DJ King's three-hour gig began at 1.30 a.m. To avoid his equipment being confiscated, he had to stop playing immediately when the gig ended and dash out of the back door. DJ King checked his wrist-watch – it was 3.45 a.m. He stared at his play-list:

Ronda Wokes and the Tri-Lunes (7.5 minutes)
Grooble Star (7.5 minutes)
The Supersonics (15 minutes)
Raddled Vipers (7.5 minutes)
Trilurian Green (7.5 minutes)

He loved every one of them. They were the hottest, newest grooves in town, never played before. But could he fit all the tracks in before the police arrived?

"I'll play it all!" he shouted into his throat mike.

The crowd cheered back.

Was DJ King's sound equipment confiscated?

1 2 3 4 5 6 7 8 9 0

Dot.com

The venture capital bankers squinted at Gayle through their thick eye-glasses. Their expressions seemed to say, "Who do you think you are, and what chance do you think you have here?" She glanced out over Manhattan. Only a few towers soared higher than this office. If she pulled off this meeting and persuaded the bankers to accept her proposal, then she could have her own office up here one day. She'd choose one with an eastern view, across Long Island.

"Er . . . Miss Spaghettini?"

Gayle wrenched her mind away from her daydream and back to the proposal. "Yes?"

The banker with a name-tag stating that he was called Aaron Banana was giving her a beady-eyed gaze. "We are wondering, looking at this proposal, how much income your website would make per day?"

Another banker, the bald one, chipped in, "You estimate a thousand visits per hour, around the clock."

The one with the thickest glasses added, "You predict that the website will make $1.50 per visit."

Gayle noticed that a worker in a yellow hard hat was hanging at one of the windows opposite, washing it with a squeegee. He must be on the eighty-fifth floor. How can he bear that? Does he ever look down? Then it occurred to her – that's how I feel! I'm dangling on the end of a thin cable! If I blow it here, I'll be back in New Jersey working at my old job, with all my dreams of success blown away.

"Well, I—" She felt panic grip her stomach. Here I am, proposing to take charge of ten million of this bank's dollars, and I can't even work out how much income I'm proposing to make per day! If I get it wrong now, I might as well get up and walk out, thought Gayle. The numbers banged around her mind like crazed ping-pong balls. She took a grip on herself.

"We're predicting . . . " Holy Moly! How many hours in a day? Don't be silly, Gayle, you know it's twenty-four. At a thousand per hour, that's . . .

"We're predicting twenty-four thousand dollars per day income, gentlemen," she said.

Do you think she raised the capital for her website?

1234567890

Drought

Drought happens when it stops raining, and there is a shortage of water. Mbangi knew that. His ancestors had been hit by drought many times. He lived on the plains in Africa, where everyone hoped for rain.

Mbangi was ambitious. He wanted to be President of his country. His mother washed his shirts whiter than white. She pressed his shorts. He worked hard at school. He practised smiling for the TV cameras. He knew they would come one day.

He smiled in the mirror at night, admiring his fine white teeth. He turned on the tap and brushed them, then flossed them, before turning off the tap. He looked at them in the mirror again – they glowed.

Then the drought came and the elders of Mbangi's village issued an order. Water was to be strictly rationed and anybody breaking the rules would be in trouble. A bath used 80 litres of water, they announced, a shower seven litres per minute. A basin of water took five litres of water. Washing your hands used 0.6 of a litre, and brushing your teeth with the tap running used two litres.

"We have to cut down on the water we use," said Mbangi's father, "or the family will be in disgrace. They have installed a meter for the village supply, so they will know exactly how much has been used."

Soon, Mbangi's shirts became less white. His shorts were stained. He felt humiliated. He thought of those TV cameras that would come one day. His whole future seemed at stake.

After three weeks, the elders met to discuss the water crisis. "The village has done very well," said the chief elder, "but we have overrun our quota by forty-two litres. We must find out who has wasted this extra water, or our supply will be cut back even further."

One of the elders who was known to be good with numbers narrowed his eyes. "I think we should speak to Mbangi," he said.

They summoned him, and Mbangi confessed.

What to?

Flight 349

Tina had just begun at Air Pacific. It was her first job, and she really wanted to get ahead. If she worked hard, she could get cheap tickets and travel the world on a budget. She longed to explore the Indian jungle, the African veld and the Amazon rainforest.

Things were going well in the reservations office, except for just one problem – her supervisor, Edwina. Edwina had problems at home – her car had been stolen and her skin had broken out. She took her problems out on the staff at Air Pacific. If Tina made one more error, Edwina would have her fired. Lately, she had taken to leaning over Tina's shoulder and correcting her every step. It was maddening. Poor Tina got flustered and made all kinds of errors she would not otherwise have made.

The call from the Australian Rowing Club came in at a busy time, and it went to Tina's extension. A top official was booking Australia's flight to England for the Henley regatta. There had been a delay, and it was extremely urgent. No other airline had room.

"So that'll be eight seats from Sydney–Kingsford Smith to London–Heathrow," Tina said brightly. She had watched the Oxford–Cambridge race on television and knew there were eight rowers in a boat.

"That'll do the men's Cup eight," the official said, "but we field several other eights as well. There's the men's A team, the ladies' eight, the ladies' B team and the Juniors."

Tina recognized a sour smell of worry and cigarettes behind her and her heart sank: it was Edwina, looming over her shoulder and listening in. She groped in the drawer for her calculator. Someone had taken it. She had to think fast.

"That's five teams," she said. " So the number of seats required is . . ."

The club official interrupted her. "Oh, and they each have a back-up rower."

He gave the flights and times required. Air Pacific's Flight 349 was a 757 jumbo jet. There were 35 seats left.

Tina made a rapid calculation in her head. She adjusted her throat-mike and said, "You've left it a bit late, sir, but fortunately we can fit you in."

What did Edwina think of that?

1 2 3 4 5 6 7 8 9 0

Flush

Ravi Ghandar was Mayor of Rinkley town, and he had big ideas.

"Rinkley is going to have an airport," he told the town council. "Rinkley International."

"But that will contribute to global warming," protested Councillor Mavis Trane, who was keen on environmental issues.

"Rinkley is going to have a big new shopping centre just outside town," Ravi announced.

"But that will encourage people to use their cars, which adds to pollution and wastes fossil fuel," Mavis Trane protested.

Mavis Trane was a big thorn in Ravi Ghandar's side. Every time he came up with a major new plan, she talked the council out of it.

Ravi Ghandar worried that he might lose the next election if he was unable to fulfil any of his promises. He would have to go back to being a nobody if that happened. What big plan could he propose that would not upset Mavis Trane?

"Rinkley is going to have a big new housing estate. Twenty thousand flats and houses. The biggest in the country," he announced proudly. "The population is growing and we need housing for everybody. Nobody can oppose that. This will put Rinkley on the map in a big way."

Mavis Trane rose from her council seat. "Imagine the water this will waste," she said. "Every time you flush the toilet, you waste ten litres of it. Just by flushing the toilet, in ten days this housing estate would empty the two million litres in an Olympic swimming pool."

The councillors gasped.

"We must vote against it," Mavis stated emphatically.

Ravi Ghandar quickly worked out the numbers and leapt to his feet. His position was on the line. "This is utter nonsense," he said firmly. "Mavis Trane has got her maths all wrong. It would take ten months, not ten days, for the new housing estate to empty an Olympic swimming pool simply by flushing the toilets. I'll stake my reputation on it."

What happened to the mayor's reputation?

1 2 3 4 5 6 7 8 9 0

Foreign Fashion

Dolores Dodds always flew to Mexico to buy her clothes. "The Mexicans have a bee-yoodiful sense of colour," she told her friends. "And everything is a real bargain because a dollar is worth around nine pesos. Look at this red silk trouser suit. I got it for only 200 dollars."

Lola Lee worked as a perfume sales representative, and she had to look smart all the time. She spent all her money on clothes, but, until she visited Dolores Dodds, she had never thought of going to Mexico for them. She listened to everything Dolores said, then bought a $450 return ticket to Acapulco.

In brilliant Mexican sunshine, Lola walked along the promenade looking at the shop windows. Everything Dolores had said was true. When you worked it out, things were a lot cheaper. You had to do a little mental arithmetic, but that cost nothing.

Lola spied a suit she liked. She entered the shop and tried the suit on. It was oat-coloured linen, with tailored pockets and elegant pleats. At 3000 pesos, it cost – let's see, she thought, 3000 divided by nine, that's about 330 dollars. A good deal!

Back in New Orleans, Lola visited Dolores and her group of friends, wearing her new suit. Everyone admired it.

"How much did you pay?" Dolores inquired.

"I got it in Acapulco," Lola said casually. "It cost 3,000 pesos. That's only 330 dollars. I've seen the same outfit here in my favourite shop for 500 dollars."

"Is this all you bought?" Dolores asked.

"Why, yes, it's just what I wanted," Lola replied.

"But my dear, that's no bargain at all!" Dolores cried out, and everyone burst out laughing, making Lola blush deeply.

What did they know?

Grand Prix

It was Dominic's first day working on a real Grand Prix race. He had started in a neighbourhood garage and vehicle testing station when he was sixteen years old. Now he was nineteen years old, and he was a wheel-fitter in the pits for Gerhard Berger, hopefully the next world champion.

The pit boss had been chief mechanic with Excel Motors for a long time. Not surprisingly, in view of the tremendous pressure of a Grand Prix race, he was a no-nonsense type. "I do my job, you do yours. You mess it up, then you won't be needed here any more," was how he had introduced Dominic to the job that day. The one thing Dominic did not intend to do was mess up – in any way. The whole village knew he was working for Gerhard Berger on this race. All his friends would be in front of the TV watching out for him. They might even see his face . . . there was a camera opposite, across the track.

"Each circuit is 5 kilometres and the race is 300 kilometres long. Our driver comes in to the pits every five circuits. You change the tyres every 50 kilometres. You should know the routine by now, you've done your training," the pit boss had told him.

Dominic had nodded at the time, springing towards the wheel bay to give the rims a last-minute polish. But now the racing cars were howling round the circuit, with screaming tyres and yelling engines. There was a reek of burning racing oil that went right to your brain. Two drivers had already spun off the track, and Dominic's head was spinning too.

He was very reluctant to ask any of his colleagues anything, for fear of giving away his nerves. But he'd lost count of where they were in the race.

Gerhard Berger went whizzing by again, and Dominic felt sure it must be time to change the wheels next time round. The switch-over would take only a couple of seconds. He simply had to know.

He plucked up his courage and tapped another Excel mechanic on the arm. "Hey, where are we at in the race?" he asked.

His colleague was far too busy watching the action to react to this question. "Halfway exactly next time round," he said.

Dominic's heart sank. Where did that get him? He still hadn't a clue whether he had to change the wheels next time Gerhard Berger appeared or not. Then he thought again. He did some rapid figuring, and jumped for the new wheels.

Did he get it right?

1 2 3 4 5 6 7 8 9 0

Herlock Shomes

I called on Herlock Shomes in Baker Street on the 25th of that month, to see if he was well.

"Ah, Watsin," he greeted me, putting aside his violin. "I'm so glad you came by. A most interesting case has come to my attention. A series of murders on a street in Kensington."

Within minutes, we were in a hansom cab, bound for London's most fashionable area. We alighted in a street of smart town houses, named Chester Avenue. We stood outside number 2, and Shomes pointed to the upper floor.

"In the main bedroom, Sir Arthur Knightley, a retired diplomat, was murdered on the 5th."

"Dreadful," I replied.

"Well," said Shomes, leading me along the avenue, "here we have another house, rather similar in appearance, where Mrs Constance Mortley was hit over the head on the 10th."

"In her bedroom?" I inquired, looking up at the first floor of number 4.

"Indeed," Shomes replied. He led me further. "Now on the 15th, in the front bedroom of this residence, Lord Rafter was killed in his sleep."

"By the same culprit, do you think?" I stared at the fated bedroom of number 8.

"The very same. Our murderer is very logical. There is a pattern to these murders."

Shomes led me further along the avenue. He stopped outside number 16. "I regret to say that an identical axe murder took place here five days ago. It is a shame I was not called in, because I could have prevented it."

"But . . . how on earth . . . ?" I was again bewildered by the genius of my detective friend.

"Fortunately," Shomes said, walking along to the door of number 32, "I am now able to intervene."

He rang and we were admitted to the residence. Shomes advised the owner, Sir Clarence Mulch, to fill his usual bed with a bolster and to sleep elsewhere for the night.

Next day, my housekeeper brought me my morning tea and the newspaper. I was astounded to read that the Chester Street murderer had been apprehended in Sir Clarence's bedroom. I hurried over to Baker Street.

"How in heaven's name did you know where and when he would strike next?" I inquired.

"Elementary, my dear Watsin," Shomes replied, picking up his violin.

What was his explanation?

Jaguars

"There is nowhere better in the world to spot jaguars than here on Lago Pongo," stated Mr Bimbleton. The fourteen children from St Mary's secondary school in Fudge-on-Cake, all gasped at the same time. They were on an educational school holiday in South America. About a dozen jaguars were draped among the branches of a tree that leaned out over the lake.

Just then, the engine of the group's old boat went bang and fell silent. There was a gurgling noise, and the boat started to list to the side. Everybody screamed, including Mr Bimbleton and Miss Blatch. The skipper shouted something in Spanish and dived into the water. His cabin boy followed.

"Look!" Raymond Spragg shouted.

There was a horrified moment as everybody watched the jaguars. They were creeping off their branches, slipping into the water, and swimming towards the sinking tour boat.

"Quiet everybody! Has anybody got a mobile that works here?" Mr Bimbleton called out. Raymond patted his pocket. "I have, sir," he replied.

Mr Bimbleton spelled out the number of the tour office and told him to call it right away.

"But they don't speak very good English, sir. They may not understand me," Raymond said. "I know, I'll send a text message, then they'll understand the situation much better."

His thumb trembled as it pressed the buttons on his mobile phone. The boat was gurgling more loudly, and he had to cling on to the rail around the side with his free hand.

"Hurry up, those jaguars are only a few minutes away," Mr Bimbleton shouted. "If we can get the helicopter to fly over, it might scare them off."

Raymond stared at the little screen on his phone. It was showing a menu he was almost too panicky to read. He clicked through the options:

* Messages
* View calls
* Text message
* Divert/Barring

Text message – that was it. He clicked on the words. Another menu appeared:

* View
* Create
* Options

Which now? Create, it must be. He clicked it.
The instruction on the screen read: "Enter message." His thumb busily hit letters as one of the jaguars snarled.

HELP SINKING NORTH END LAKE JAGUAR COMING

Raymond stared in horror at the screen. It said: "40 characters max." The jaguar snarled again, closer this time.
   He pressed the back arrow and goggled at the message. He counted 35 characters. PHEW!! He entered the number and pressed 'Send'. He crossed his fingers and watched the jaguars swimming towards him as the boat leaned further into the water. Everybody was screaming now.

Did the message get through?

1 2 3 4 5 6 7 8 9 0

Lifeboat

Southern Air flight 132 hit the Atlantic ocean at 1.35 a.m. on a cloudy night. It was pandemonium in the darkness on board. Passengers groped for their life-jackets under the seats. They scrambled across each other seeking the exits. Those lucky enough to find life-jackets, get to an exit and slide down the escape chute, fell into icy water and shivered.

Through the dark, Della Ramone saw the vague mass of the airliner sinking. She frantically paddled away, and avoided being sucked down with it. Bobbing on the water, she heard others blowing their whistles, and searched for her own.

She heard voices behind her, and felt hands grasping. They hauled her aboard a life raft. Someone handed her a flash light. She took it and looked around. She saw other faces, gripped by fear and cold. She recognized one of the cabin staff, Molly.

"There are so many to rescue," Molly cried. "Let's hurry!"

The beam from Della's light fell on a label sewn on to the side. It said:

DYNO SELF-INFLATING LIFE RAFT CORP.
Made in China
Maximum capacity: 1,000 kilos
Warning! Deadly danger: DO NOT OVERLOAD.

"Here are some more survivors," Molly shouted, shining her light over the side. "Nobody lasts more than a few minutes in water this cold. Come on, help me get them aboard!"

Della stared at the label. One thousand kilos. She shone her light round the raft again. There were sixteen survivors aboard, including herself. Seven men and nine women. What would their average weight be? About 70 kilos she estimated. She gasped and shone her light overboard. The sea was lapping high, threatening to wash over the side. "Molly, stop!" she shouted. "We're going to sink if you take any more!"

What happened?

$1^2 3^4 5^6 7^8 9_0$

A Million

Tara was in love. Jamie was taller, nicer and funnier than anyone she knew. She longed for him to admire her. She felt certain that they should be together.

Imagine how Tara felt when Jamie phoned and asked her to be his back-up on the prime-time TV quiz show *Million-Pound Mind*. And imagine how disappointed she was when he reached the final round without consulting her once.

When the night of the final came, she could hardly face it. Only her friends' and her mother's persuasion made her sit by the phone yet again, watching Jamie answer the questions on TV.

She had to admit it was exciting. Jamie could actually win a million pounds that night if he kept his cool. The audience was in a feverish state, screaming and cheering him on. The tension was mounting. But each time Jamie got an answer right, Tara got more despondent. She did not care how rich he got, if it was without her help.

When Jamie got to £950,000, she reached out to switch off the TV but her mother stopped her.

"So, Jamie," said the quiz master. "Will you take the £950,000, or answer another question?"

Jamie grinned. "I'll take the question."

The audience cheered, and Tara groaned.

"Be patient, dear," said her mum.

"Right," said the quiz master, reading from his card. "For a million pounds, then. It's four o'clock in the afternoon in Britain. What time is it in Hollywood, USA?"

"Eight hours behind," Tara whispered, covering her eyes and waiting for Jamie's answer.

No answer came. She peeked through her fingers. Jamie was blinking.

"Would you like to ask a friend?" prompted the quiz master.

Tara screamed. Her mum jumped up and down. The audience went nuts.

"I think I would," Jamie said.

Tara's telephone rang.

What answer did she give?

1 2 3 4 5 6 7 8 9 0

Partners

Herbie and Horace were old pals. Each thought he was wilier than a fox, and twice as wily as the other.

One day Herbie got hold of an old car. "I'll tell you what," he told Horace. "For your share, you can pay just half what I paid for it. That'll be a bargain from your point of view – only half-price for a top-quality car."

Horace thought it over. "If she breaks down," he said, "I'll walk halfway to the garage and you can walk the other."

"Sounds good to me," replied his friend.

They shook on it, and got into the car. Herbie was about to turn the key and start up, when he changed his mind. Sitting back, he eyed his friend shrewdly. "What about fuel?" he said.

Horace thought it over. "I'll pay to fill her when she's half-full," he said.

Herbie narrowed his eyes and examined his scheming friend. You could almost hear the numbers clicking around in his brain. He sucked his teeth, and a clever gleam came into his eyes. "And I fill her up when she's only half-empty?"

Horace considered. "Right," he said.

Herbie twisted the key and roared the engine. "All right!" he shouted, and let in the clutch.

Which friend paid more at the service station?

Petrol

Richard Green was an ambitious civil servant – make that very ambitious. He was facing a parliamentary committee. It included some of the sharpest brains in the House. He could not afford a single error. It was even more vital than usual that he did not make a slip because he was on television – live national television, on the *Nine O'Clock News*, with an audience of about 10 million. But really, only one person counted – Sir Ralph Huntley-Palmer, a big chief in the civil service. He'd be watching, without a shadow of a doubt. And if he saw Richard Green make a mistake, then that'd be that. His goose would be cooked, or however the saying goes.

The subject of the committee concerned the fate of planet Earth itself. Humans were burning up the atmosphere at a tremendous rate. The climate was affected. People were alarmed by it. And now it was Richard's moment to speak.

"Mr Green, the petrol burnt by our nation in 1979 was 29 million tonnes." It was Clegg Williams speaking. Richard's nerves twanged. He felt a vein in his neck bulging, hoped it would not appear on the television screen. "In 1998, the yearly figure was 37 million tonnes. Could you tell the committee, do you consider that to be an increase in petrol consumption?"

Richard looked desperately for a trick in the question. He could not for the life of him find one. Surely even a member of parliament could work out the answer? He took the plunge. "An increase, Mr Williams."

"Of how much, Mr Green?"

Richard froze. He could not remember the first number. Or even the second. Madly, he wrestled with numbers. He loosened his collar. He coughed nervously. Surely this was making him look terrible on TV? "Nine million tonnes, Mr Williams."

Did Richard's career survive?

1 2 3 4 5 6 7 8 9 0

Pop

The band Spl*t consisted of the triplets Chico, Rico and Tica. The spelling was Tica's idea. "It looks different," she said. Chico and Rico nodded, as they always did to Tica's suggestions. The Spl*t album went platinum. They toured the world. Then they toured it again. Then they rested.

Tica bought a palace in a sunny country far from the grimy city where the triplets had been brought up. The palace had 26 bedrooms.

Tica decided to have a small get-together so she flew 58 people over for the weekend.

"What will everyone eat?" her boyfriend asked. His name was Pl>>g. Spelling it that way was a silly idea, because nobody ever saw it written down, but he didn't want to be left out.

"A caterer," she said. She didn't mean you actually ate the caterer, but . . . well, you get the idea.

Ronni Bake, the caterer, arrived that evening. At supper, they discussed the party. It was Ronni's big chance for a breakthrough in her career. She enthused while they ate.

"I see an explosion of green – green avocadoes, green bananas, limes, apples, cucumbers, kiwi fruit, celery, chicken . . ."

"Green chicken?" Pl>>g interrupted.

"An explosion?" mused Tica, imagining the effect on the guests.

But Ronni effortlessly talked them into it. Then she started to work furiously hard. Her plan was to present the plates of food in pairs, one set for each couple. The "boy's" setting would be decorated with spears of celery and arrows of sprouting bamboo. The "girl's" would be adorned with peacock feathers and cream.

Ronni calculated that the guests required 27 pairs of settings. It was a tall order, because Ronni wanted such food items as frizzy lettuce, unripe walnuts in their skins and chicken dyed green. But, everything has its price, and with her budget, Ronni had no real trouble getting what she needed. Whatever the merchants could not provide, Ronni had flown in by private jet.

The trouble came when the banquet was prepared, the band started playing and everybody came in from the swimming pool to eat.

What was the problem?

1234567890

Princes

Prince Ibo was born into a very rich and noble family. He went to an expensive private school in Switzerland, which was positioned conveniently next to his father's bank. After lights out, he used his stack of credit cards to play snap with his friends. He stuffed his pillow full of bundled up bank notes to make it comfortable. He bribed teachers to give him top marks.

Prince Ahmed went to the same school as Prince Ibo. He was so rich that he kept three huge cars outside the school.

The two boys were rivals. Somehow they heard that the swankiest hotel in the world had the latest computer games installed in its rooms. These games were very difficult to get, and both boys wanted them more than anything else they could think of.

When term ended on the eighth of the month, Prince Ibo made an excuse to his parents and checked in to the exclusive Hotel Lancester on London's Park Lane. A room there cost five thousand pounds a night. "But there is a different computer game in each room, and a new one is put in the room every day until the day you check out," Ibo told his envious friends.

He bribed the manager to show him the register. It showed that Prince Ahmed had reserved three rooms. "Then I will take twelve," Ibo stated.

The manager bowed and made a note. "Will your highness be staying until the morning of the 20th, like Prince Ahmed?" he inquired.

"Alas," Prince Ibo replied. "I have to return home on the 11th." But I am reserving far more rooms, so I will have many more movies than poor Ahmed, he gloated to himself.

Was he right?

Princesa

The actress Princesa's first film, *Donna*, scored big. It scored so big that Princesa was able to move from a bungalow in an ordinary part of Los Angeles straight into a swanky place in Beverly Hills.

The real estate lady she contacted, Lotti Wall, talked a lot. She talked Princesa into buying the first house she saw. It had arched doors and windows and curved red tiles on the roof. It had an interior courtyard with palm trees and a fountain. There was a patio at the back with a swimming pool that had a sweeping view of the city below. The pool lit up at night, and there was a triple-deck diving board, plus a trampoline you could dive from. As you dived from the top board, it felt as though you were diving across Los Angeles. The kitchen was in the conservatory, and the bedroom had two bathrooms.

"I'll take it," Princesa said. "How much?"

"A lot," said Lotti Wall. "But you can afford it, believe me." She held out the printed details for Princesa to read. The price written there was $11000000.

"My, that's reasonable," Princesa said, handing the details back. "Now, about the furniture."

"I can handle that," Lotti said quickly. "The very latest in interior decor throughout. You'll love it."

"When?" Princesa asked.

Lotti paused for only a second. "Tomorrow?" she said.

Princesa moved in next evening. Her agent came round, plus a group of friends and some other hangers-on. Her boyfriend, the rock star Shane Doowop, was on tour in the Far East.

Next morning, exploring her new place, she found the garage. It had stalls for five vehicles. She took out her mobile phone and called her accountant.

"Ronnie, I'm in my new garage," she told him. "I forgot about cars. I need five nice new ones to fill this place. Maybe make that four, so I've got a space for a guest."

"Sorry, babe, no can do," said the voice of her accountant. "You cleaned yourself out buying that house. In fact, you're three million dollars in debt, and I'd say you've got a big problem looming at the bank."

The blood drained from Princesa's face. She staggered against the wall. "Wha-a-a-t? The place was a snip at a million one," she said.

Where had she gone wrong?

1 2 3 4 5 6 7 8 9 0

Rhapsody

Zoran Zapata, the world-famous composer, strode onto the stage. Behind him, the orchestra started foot-stamping. In the concert hall, the audience jumped to their feet and cheered. He bowed. He went to the podium and climbed the stairs. High above everybody, he turned and surveyed the musicians. They would astound humanity with his new work, *Rhapsody in Five Movements*.

An expectant silence fell. The orchestra watched him closely. Frowning, he raised his white baton, drew it back, and rammed it violently towards the heavens. A tremendous opening chord blasted across the hall, shaking the windows and rattling the glasses at the bar.

Zapata immediately pressed a finger to his lips, and the music fell to a tiny tinkling. But something else had distracted the maestro – his exquisitely sensitive ears had detected a sharp 'ping' from his suit-trouser braces. That wretched laundry at the Ritzy Hotel! They must have failed to repair the worn threads of his buttons! His mind raced. Each movement of the Rhapsody opened with that shattering chord. He must thrust his baton to the skies each time. But what if his trousers fell down?

Breaking out in a sweat, he vaguely waved the players on, and desperately counted the buttons in his mind's eye. Two on each brace at the front, and two at the back. One button had already been lost so that left five buttons. Only four movements left, and their four thunderous opening chords. At one burst button per chord, he would narrowly survive.

Breathing a sigh of relief, the maestro found his place in the music and continued.

What kind of reviews did he get?

Roberto

Roberto wore a smart suit, a silk tie and a rose on his lapel. His shoes were brilliantly polished, his hair was greased down, and he wore a cowboy hat at an angle. He approached the El Dorado Hotel on the smartest street in Hollywood in a luxury taxi, even though he had journeyed from just around the corner. When he got out, he turned and paid the driver in loose change – much of it worthless foreign coins. The uniformed doorman was impressed, and called a porter to take Roberto's suitcase, which was weighed down inside with a bag of potatoes.

Roberto went to the desk clerk and took the most expensive suite available. He followed the bellboy to the rooms, tipped him with fake banknotes, jumped up and down on the bed a few times, and took a bath. From deep within a mountain of foam, he telephoned room service and ordered pizza, doughnuts and ice cream, plus a strawberry milkshake.

Later, he watched three movies on TV before sleeping soundly between satin sheets in the four-poster bed.

Next morning, he had champagne and fruit yoghurt on his terrace, overlooking the city, wearing the hotel bath-robe.

He passed two more days in similar style, using the hotel pool, snooker room and gym, and enjoyed two more restful nights on pillows of down.

When he had enjoyed all that the El Dorado had to offer, his clothes had been laundered, his shoes polished, and he wore in his lapel a flower that had come with brunch, he decided to check out.

He handed in his door key, and gave the name of a guest whom he had noticed checking in late the day before, when different staff had been on the desk. "It's just the one night," he said confidently.

The desk clerk looked at Roberto, thinking quickly.

Did he rumble him?

1 2 3 4 5 6 7 8 9 0

Shots

Willy Fantoni went cross-eyed threading wire into widgets at a widget factory. He got a pair of glasses, but they brought his ears out in a rash. So he turned to a life of crime.

It was Chicago in the 1920s, and Willy used his savings to buy a suit, a pair of dark glasses to hide his eyes and a solid six-shooter.

On his first stick-up job, he went into a petrol-station office and fired in all directions. The cashier trembled and threw the contents of the cash register at Willy. The money fell out at his feet.

"Dis is easy," Willy told his buddies later, waving a wad of banknotes.

A couple of his buddies were cross-eyed, too, having worked threading wire into widgets at the same factory as Willy. That night, they talked about Willy's success in crime.

"Ev'body's doin' it," said Lou Polletta. "Dis is Chicago in de nine'een twennies. Anyway, whut else kin a cross-eyed guy do?"

They bought big pistols just like Willy's and pairs of dark glasses. They offered to help him do stick-ups. He thought about it, and said, "Duh, OK."

The three partners quickly became notorious for shooting in all directions. They struck fear into the heart of Chicago's petrol stations. Newspaper headlines called them the Shades Gang. Nobody was quite sure how many members the gang had, because they were always bumping into doors and walking in wrong directions. It became a much-asked question. The headlines demanded: Why doesn't anyone know how many there are in the Shades Gang?

The mayor, Hyde Formaldi, boiled with rage. He hammered his desk. He shouted out of the window. Finally, he thought of talking to his police chief, Chuck Smith.

Chuck took it easy. He went slowly down to the latest Shades Gang crime scene. It was fenced off. Guys in white coats were dusting for fingerprints. He looked round the bare walls of the petrol station office. They were peppered with bullet holes.

"How many bullet holes we got here, boys?" he inquired casually. They told him that there were fourteen in the walls, one in the counter, two in the window and one in the floor.

Chuck took his time making a calculation, turned and ambled back to his prowl-car.

Down at City Hall, he faced Mayor Formaldi, who was still bright pink, with steam rising from his bald head.

"The jokers in shades. There's t'ree of 'em." Chief Smith told his boss.

Mayor Formaldi got re-elected. Chief Smith got a secret hundred-grand bonus.

How did Chuck Smith work out the number of members in the gang?

$$1\,2\,3\,4\,5\,6\,7\,8\,9\,0$$

Sleep

England's House of Commons debating chamber has few windows. Sir Archibald Gracious MP noticed this for the Nth time as he awoke from a nap on the back benches. "Why do they expect us to do without light?" he grumbled to himself.

He burped, and looked round guiltily. Lunch had been long, and substantial. As usual, he had come to the debating chamber to pass out for an hour or two. It was the quietest, most boring, place in London.

Suddenly, there was a bit of a bustle. Sir Archibald pulled himself upright, adjusted his moustache, fitted his monocle back into his left eye, and examined the floor. He was astonished to see that the Prime Minister was preparing to speak.

"My government is deeply disturbed," he heard the Prime Minister say, "by the Chief Medical Officer's report."

Report? What report? Sir Archibald mumbled to himself. He looked around the house. Four MPs were napping opposite. Two unknown members of the cabinet were seated behind the Prime Minister, nodding gravely for the TV cameras. On his own front bench, two schoolgirls were pretending to be important members of the Opposition. Three of his friends were asleep nearby.

"We held an emergency meeting of the cabinet this morning to discuss the report," the Prime Minister went on. "We decided that further research is needed. We must not act in panic. What are the facts? The Chief Medical Officer argues that our nation is asleep for one-third of the time. She produces some evidence, but we are not fully satisfied that she has made her case. We are setting up a royal commission to look into the matter."

Sir Archibald tottered wearily into the lobby. His colleague Wells Tucker was there. He greeted Sir Archibald, who demanded to know what the Prime Minister was wittering on about.

"Well, it's this claim that the whole country is asleep half the time, or rather one-third of the time. Apparently, it's costing business a fortune. We're facing ruin. Something has to be done."

Sir Archibald drew himself to his full height (a head shorter than Wells Tucker). "I have never heard of such a ridiculous theory in my life. I intend to put a stop to this nonsense once and for all. I will conduct a national campaign for common sense."

Yes, he thought as he marched towards his office, suddenly filled with new energy. I shall explode back on to the scene. I will be on the *Nine O'Clock News*. I shall once again be a contender for party leader. I must phone Daphne and let her know. She will need a new outfit for garden parties.

He promptly called a news conference and announced his new campaign. "It is called Nation Awake," he declared. "We intend to put an end to this mad theory that our wonderful British people spend a third of their time flat out asleep. It is upsetting people."

"What action do you intend to take first?" the BBC reporter asked.

"We want the Chief Medical Officer to resign," Sir Archibald stated.

How did Sir Archibald's campaign do?

Strangled

Professor Penfold was on Flight 345 when it reached LAX airport in Los Angeles. But he did not rise from his seat and reach for his hand luggage in the overhead compartments. He was still there when the cabin staff made their departing check. They soon found he was dead. The transport police officer they called noticed the signs of strangling.

An incident room was set up at Terminal 12. Heading the murder investigation was Lieutenant Karl P. Kramer.

"Penfold was sitting alone in his row. It looks like someone got talking to him and then strangled him. The professor was a great man, a key figure in the campaign to ban smoking," he told his officers. "We have drawn up a profile of the suspect. We are looking for a chain-smoker, with stained fingers and teeth, clothes reeking of fumes, a nasty hacking cough and a rough voice. Oh, and our suspect will almost certainly be connected with a tobacco company. Go get 'em, team!"

Officer Tricia Polenski intended to get noticed in this case. She wanted Kramer's job so bad she could taste it. Nobody was going to hold her back from a high-flying career.

She took a look at the layout of a Boeing 777 jumbo jet.
Two seats at each window end of the row, three between
the aisles. She scanned the list of passengers that fitted the
profile. The main suspect was a person named Deek Troy
Yonk III. Officer Polenski decided to call Deek Troy Yonk III in
for questioning.

77

A beautiful woman entered the room. Tricia approached her. Deek Yonk stank of fumes. Her fingers were stained. Her lovely teeth were stained. She wheezed when she breathed. Plus, she worked in cigarette sales.

"So, Deek, how come your second name is Troy?" Tricia demanded.

"My mother thought it was a girl's name, and why not?" Deek replied.

"Well, I guess that's fair enough," Tricia admitted. "Now, what time did you join flight 345? What number was your ticket? What number was your seat? How many movies did you watch?"

"I joined the flight in Chicago at 11.45," Deek said. "I have no idea of my ticket number, but I remember my seat number was row 33 seat H."

Tricia stared at her, silently counting. "You're under arrest for murder in the first degree," she said.

What made Tricia's mind up?

1 2 3 4 5 6 7 8 9 0

Supermarket

Vasto supermarkets were started by a stallholder in a street market in East London. By the beginning of the 21st century the board of directors had lost count of their stores, there were so many all over the world.

Farah Shah, the head of Vasto, wore a pinstriped suit, rode in a pinstriped car and never had a penny to hand (somebody else dealt with that). When she said "Beans", the bean-makers trembled. When she said "Biscuits", farmers on their tractors stopped and rolled their eyes. When Farah Shah went into petrol, Vasto promptly became the world's biggest petrol station. Her Vasto bank became the biggest overnight. The day Vasto launched a website, it became the most visited on earth.

One day Farah Shah announced a new hyper-dooper-store. She boasted that its car park was big enough to park every car in Birmingham.

Strangely for such a powerful businesswoman, she was hen-pecked at home. Her daughter, Rezah, aged twelve, was bossy. She probably took after her mother.

"How big is the car park?" demanded Rezah.

"Well, it has fifteen thousand parking spaces. That's enough to take every car in Birmingham, so I just . . ."

"But that's nonsense, Mum," Rezah shouted. "Your car park could only take one-twentieth of Birmingham's cars."

Her mother thought for a second. "Oh dear, does Birmingham really have that many cars?" she said.

How many did she mean?

1 2 3 4 5 6 7 8 9 0

Telephone

Special Agent Dale Plant stared at the evidence, an e-mail printout which read:

You will collect the deckchairs at the baseball bat at 2300 on the 4th and hand them to T16.

Plant knew "deckchairs" was code for a cargo of smuggled contraband. He knew "baseball bat" was the old Pier 12 at the abandoned docks. He knew the 4th was yesterday. Trouble was, his officers had arrested three suspects at 2300 hours at the scene, instead of one. How was he to tell which one was the king-pin code-named T16?

He scratched his head, and took a deep swig of coffee to try to boost his brain. He'd pulled out the files on the three suspects. They were laid out before him.

Mungo Rhinegold
Sex: Male
Age: 28
Address: 4293 West 34th
Telephone: 224 1412

Alita Paulson
Sex: Female
Age: 23
Address: 1342 West 28th
Telephone: 996 4848

Zbigniew Jablonski
Sex: Male
Age: 35
Address: 28 Main St, Apt 4
Telephone: 887 1542

Plant read them carefully, playing around with the numbers. He stared at the code again: T16. There was a clue there somewhere.

Suddenly, the penny dropped. He went out of his office into the squad room. "Hey, Maloney!" he shouted.

He ordered Maloney to go to the cells and bring up a suspect for questioning right away.

Which one?

1 2 3 4 5 6 7 8 9 0

Trapeze

Bonita worked with her family in the circus. She helped her mother in the caravan and she made hot drinks for the ticket office. But one day, her father, Rosio, came to her bedroom first thing in the morning and said, "Get up, Bonita, it's your first rehearsal."

Bonita's heart pounded, and she ran in to tell her mother the good news that she was joining the Flying Burritos at last.

All the Burrito family members were trapeze artists. Their timing was superb. They even did the washing up together, tossing the cups and plates around backhand. They were superb athletes. Chico Burrito, Bonita's brother, could vault a horse and jump through the open window of the family car, right into the driving seat. And now Bonita was going to be trained too.

Every day she spent hours working with her father and mother on low trapezes set up outside the Big Top. Then she practised on the high trapezes. At last she was ready to perform.

Bonita's mother and father had thought of a special trick to showcase Bonita, who was ten years old. The drum would roll, and the ringmaster would boom over the loudspeakers, "And now little Bonita Burrito, only ten years old, will perform a back-flip in mid-air, the youngest person in the world ever to do so."

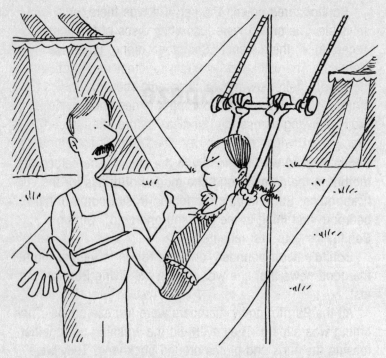

On the night, her father and mother gave her a special reminder, "Remember," they said, "there is a net but you cannot rely on it. You could easily put your leg or your head through it and be badly injured. Do not make a mistake, OK?"

Bonita assured them she would get it right. The family act was one of the best. Their wild flips from trapeze to trapeze, near the roof of the Big Top, always got the crowd excited. Bonita began by holding trapezes for the others, joining the flourish after each trick. But at last, the drum rolled especially loudly, and the ringmaster made his announcement. Her turn had come.

Bonita stared down. The net, if it was there, was invisible. The crowd were just white discs of frightened faces, far in the distance. She stood alone, under the spotlight. The whole family clung together in a spotlight beam 50 metres away, watching her. The drum rolled harder. Her mind raced. How many times should she let the trapeze swing across the darkness before she jumped? Nerves had wiped her memory clean. Was it three times? Yes, three. Bonita was sure now.

She pulled the trapeze towards her, and let it go.

What happened?

1 2 3 4 5 6 7 8 9 0

Window

Ray Pachundra was a gardener. Gardeners are particularly intelligent people. They have to remember difficult names such as *tigridia pavonia* (Tiger flower). They have to remember all the dates for planting, picking and weeding different plants. They have to know what will grow where, and how. They have to know about seeds. They have to understand delicate operations such as grafting. And they have to use what is called a "green finger", meaning that they are good at making things grow.

Although Ray Pachundra deserved to be famous for what he did, he was just an ordinary gardener with an ordinary pick-up truck and a list of customers who came out and gave him a cup of tea now and then. But, one day he did become famous.

Wally Bunter, a cowboy builder, was responsible for his fame. Some builders are called cowboys because they ride about doing the odd bit of work, then gallop off into the sunset, leaving you in the lurch. That's exactly what happened with Ray's employer, Mrs Fortescue. She was a kind old lady who wanted to fit her house with central heating and insulation. Wally knocked on her door one day and offered to do the work. She got the price and told him to go ahead.

Basically, Wally smashed the house up. He knocked walls down. He ripped out bits of roof. He tore ceilings away. Soon, the house was little more than a shell, and Mrs Fortescue had to move in with her sister a mile away. Wally disappeared.

Then Friday came round, the day Ray did the garden. He arrived in his pick-up truck and stared at the house. It looked a mess. The second-storey windows four metres above his garden were missing. The roof had gaping holes in it. The insides had been gutted. He shook his head and shrugged. There was no explaining the way these builders went about things.

But Ray soon forgot about the house. He was busy with a new rose garden he was making for Mrs Fortescue. He had planned it out carefully. There were to be two rows of rose plants stretching at right angles away from the rear of the house. He had aligned each row with the two pairs of upstairs and downstairs windows. The rose plants would start one metre from the wall, and be planted one metre apart.

He worked on the flowerbeds for a while, then he fetched the plants from his pick-up. Starting with the row on the east side, he bent over and planted the first rose. He tamped it well down and watered it. Then he moved forward to the next one.

It took him five minutes to plant each rose. After a while, he stood up to stretch his back and check whether it was time to pour a cup of tea from his Thermos. He'd been planting for twenty minutes. Tea could wait.

At that moment, he heard an alarming creak. It was followed by a wrenching sound. Ray looked over his shoulder. The rear wall of the house was falling towards him. For an instant, he thought of running for it, but a gut instinct told him he wouldn't make it. The wall would crush him to death.

He looked at his partial row of roses, made a quick calculation, and stood his ground.

Why did he become famous that day?

Answers

Air Show

The bang was caused by the Prang aeroplane breaking the sound barrier. It must, therefore, have been travelling at a speed greater than Mach 1.

Barbells

The barbell weighed 130 kilos and not the 110 kilos Herbie had expected. The bar crashed onto his knees as he tried to lift it and he had to retire from weightlifting. He decided to teach flower-arranging instead.

Bathtime

Yes, Minh was correct in his calculations. 20,000 litres of water in total ÷ 200 litres of water used in 2 baths per day = 100 days. Ho bought a modern bath that used 60 litres instead. His skin soon cleared up.

The Blurby Case

The hotel had a row of eight rooms along the stair side. They were given even numbers, so they ran from 2 to 16. There was no number 18.

Canyon

Rita's mistake was to use a two-handed grip whilst she was waiting for the helicopter to arrive. The helicopter was due to arrive in 25 minutes, 0.4 seconds after she would have lost her two-handed grip. Rita forgot that if she held on for as long as she could with just one hand, then with the other, she could last for 28.6 minutes (14.3 x 2). The rescuers would have had 3.6 minutes to spare.

Cat
Toby answered correctly that a cat has 18 toes altogether (5 x 2 = 10 at the front + 4 x 2 = 8 at the back).

Change
No, the customer really did want change. He obtained a ten, a five and five singles in return for a twenty. Jo had no need to worry.

Concert
They narrowly made it to the concert. Dad based his assertion on a quick estimate, by rounding off 29 miles to 30, and 62 mph to 60. Travelling 60 miles in an hour, he would cover 30 miles in half an hour. As they were actually travelling slightly faster than this, and had a slightly shorter distance to travel, they would have arrived within the half hour.

The Dare
Yes, Maureen's modesty remained intact. She sliced her jeans in half across the knees.

DJ King
No, his playlist ended right on time.

Dot.com
Gayle mistakenly based her calculations on $1.00, instead

of $1.50. If her site was visited 1,000 times in an hour, making $1.50 each visit, as she proposed, then in 24 hours, it would be visited 24,000 times, providing a daily income of $36,000 (24,000 hrs x $1.50 per hour).

However, her website idea was such a good one that the bankers were keen to invest anyway. A year later, she sold the site for $1.4 billion.

Drought

Mbangi confessed to cleaning his teeth with the tap running. The overrun of 42 litres exactly matched the two litres per day wasted by brushing his teeth with the tap running for the three weeks or 21 days of rationing (2 litres per day x 21 days = 42 litres). Because Mbangi was honest, he was not disgraced. He went on to become Vice-President.

Flight 349

Edwina was not impressed. There were five teams of eight (5 x 8 = 40) plus one back-up rower per team (40 + 5) so there were 45 seats needed altogether. Tina miscalculated. With only 35 seats left on the aeroplane, the Australian Rowing Club was 10 seats short.

Flush

The mayor's reputation was damaged. He should have quickly worked out that Mavis Trane's maths was right (10 litres x 20,000 = 200,000 x 10 days = 2,000,000 or 2 million litres). The housing estate would indeed have emptied an Olympic swimming pool of 2 million litres in 10 days.

Foreign Fashion
Lola had forgotten to count the cost of her ticket.

Grand Prix
Yes, Dominic did get it right. His colleague told him that it was coming up for halfway through the race, so the drivers must have done nearly 150 km of the 300 km long race. Dominic had to change wheels every 50 km, so 150 km would be the point for a third wheel-change.

Herlock Shomes
Shomes observed that the murders took place every five days, at house numbers that doubled each time.

Jaguars
Sadly, no. Raymond forgot that he had to count the characters and the spaces. There were 41 characters including the spaces. The message did not get through.

Lifeboat
Sadly, Della's quick calculation was correct. At an average weight of 70 kilos, sixteen people weighed over 1,000 kilos (16 x 70 = 1120). The life raft could not take any more survivors.

A Million
If it is 4 p.m. in Britain, 16:00 hours by the 24 hour clock, and Hollywood is eight hours behind, then (16hr - 8hr = 8hr), it must be 8 a.m. in Hollywood. Tara gave the correct answer and Jamie made a million. He and Tara married soon after.

Partners
Both Herbie and Horace paid the same amount of money at the service station.

Petrol
Yes, although Richard's answer was wrong. The increase in petrol consumption was eight million tonnes (37 million tonnes - 29 million tonnes). However, Sir Ralph Huntley-Palmer could not possibly allow the nation to think one of his civil servants could not do mental arithmetic. He had the figures fixed, said Richard was in the right, and promoted him.

Pop
Ronni miscalculated the number of settings needed. There were 60 people eating, including Tica and Pl>>g, but Ronni had only allowed for 54 people at the party (27 pairs of settings). The dinner party was therefore 6 settings short. Ronni's career suffered.

Princes
Ibo was wrong. Both he and Prince Ahmed would have the same amount of computer games. Ibo had reserved 12 rooms for 3 nights (12 x 3 = 36) so he would have 36 computer games if a new game was added each day, except the day he left. Prince Ahmed had reserved 3 rooms for 12 nights (3 x 12 = 36) so he would also have 36 games at the end of his stay.

Princesa
Lotti Wall cunningly left the commas out of the house price. Princesa read it as $1.1 million. In fact, it was $11 million. She had to sell the place a few weeks later, but she made a profit on it anyway.

Rhapsody

The reviews were all bad. In his haste, the maestro miscalculated. He assumed that he would still have one button left at the end of the last movement. But one button could not support his trousers. At least two were required, one front and one back. The trousers were bound to fall on the fifth movement's opening chord. They did. Zapata was a laughing stock and he lost his nerve.

Roberto

He did. Foolish Roberto's room number was written on his door key.

Shots

The gang used six-shooters, meaning each gun held six bullets. There were 18 bullet holes altogether, so, assuming each member of the gang used all the bullets in their gun, there must have been three people in the gang (18 ÷ 6 = 3).

Sleep

Sir Archibald's campaign went badly. People sleep for about eight hours out of 24, or one-third of the time (24 ÷ 8 = 3). This means that, in a year, you sleep for about four months. Sir Archibald returned to napping on the back benches. Daphne never got her new outfit.

Strangled

The airliner had rows of seven seats (2-3-2). Row 33, therefore, only went from seat A to seat G (seventh letter of the alphabet). There was no seat 33H. Deek Yonk was lying. She later confessed to the crime.

Supermarket

Farah Shah quickly worked out that if 15,000 were one-tenth of Birmingham's cars, there would be 150,000 (15,000 x 10). So, if it were one-twentieth it would be twice as many, i.e. 300,000.

Telephone

Mungo Rhinegold. Plant guessed that T stood for telephone. When he added up the digits of each telephone number, he found that Rhinegold's totalled 16, hence the code name T16. This evidence was crucial in the trial. Rhinegold was sentenced to 28 years in prison for smuggling.

Trapeze

Three swings put Bonita's trapeze on the far side, with her family. She jumped and grabbed on to nothing. It was a terrifying fall, but fortunately she bounced harmlessly in the safety net. She went on to have three children, who all joined the Flying Burritos.

Window

Ray rapidly worked out that, after 20 minutes at five minutes per rose, he had planted four roses, three metres between the first and the last. There was another metre between the first rose and the wall. It meant Ray was standing four metres from the wall. The row of roses was aligned with the upstairs window, which was four metres off the ground. The wall thundered to the ground around Ray, who passed clean through the empty window, unhurt, if covered in dust. A neighbour videoed the event. Ray explained how he'd done it on the local TV news, and the national TV news carried the story that evening. Then TV news bulletins all over the world picked up the story, and Ray was world-famous for a day.

A selected list of titles available from Macmillan and Pan Books

The prices shown below are correct at the time of going to press. However, Macmillan Publishers reserve the right to show new retail prices on covers which may differ from those previously advertised.

Absolutely Mental 1 Rowland Morgan	0 330 48172 X	£2.99
Number Crunchers: Brain Bafflers Rowland Morgan	0 330 36783 8	£1.99
Number Crunchers: Brain Bafflers and Mind Boggers Rowland Morgan	0 330 48013 8	£2.99
Alien Puzzles Sandy Ransford	0 330 39220 4	£2.99
School Jokes Sandy Ransford	0 330 39222 0	£2.99

All Macmillan titles can be ordered at your local bookshop or are available by post from:

Book Service by Post
PO Box 29, Douglas, Isle of Man IM99 1BQ

Credit cards accepted. For details:
Telephone: 01624 675137
Fax: 01624 670923
E-mail: bookshop@enterprise.net

Free postage and packing in the UK.
Overseas customers: add £1 per book (paperback)
and £3 per book (hardback).